big band hi

as performed by will young, gareth gates, darius and others

Thirteen arrangements for voice, piano and guitar, with CD backing tracks

Published 2002
© International Music Publications Limited
Griffin house, 161 Hammersmith Road, London, W6 8BS, England

Edited by Chris Harvey
Music arranged by Artemis Music Ltd
Photography ©2002 Redferns Music Picture Library / Rex Features International

big band hits

as performed by will young, gareth gates, darius and others

Get Happy

Words and Music by Harold Arlen and Ted Koehler

Lyrics:

For-get your trou-bles come on get hap - py You bet-ter chase all your cares a - way

Sing hal - le - lu - jah come on get hap - py Get read - y for the judge-ment day,

troubles___ get hap-py___ your cares fly___ a-way shout hal-le-

-lu-jah___ get hap-py___ get read-y___ for your judge-ment

day.

Sun is

Beyond The Sea

Original Words and Music by Charles Trenet and Albert Lasry
English Words by Jack Lawrence

Let There Be Love

Words by Ian Grant
Music by Lionel Rand

Let there be you, let there — be me, — let there be

Let there__ be cuc - koos,____ a lark and a dove,____

but first__ of all please,____ let there be love.

(piano solo)

Mack The Knife

Words by Bertholt Brecht
Music by Kurt Weill
Translation by Marc Blitzstein

Lyrics:

1. Oh the shark babe, has such teeth dear, and he shows them pearly white. Just a
(2.) shark bites with his teeth dear, scar-let bil-lows start to spread. Fan-cy

Ev'ry Time We Say Goodbye

Words and Music by Cole Porter

I Get A Kick Out Of You

Words and Music by Cole Porter

I've Got You Under My Skin

Words and Music by Cole Porter

That Ole Devil Called Love Again

Words and Music by Allan Roberts and Doria Fisher

I Won't Dance

Words by Oscar Hammerstein II, Dorothy Fields, Otto Harbach and Jimmy McHugh
Music by Jerome Kern

47

When you dance you're___ charm-ing and you're gen-tle,___

Night And Day

Words and Music by Cole Porter

Cheek To Cheek

Words and Music by Irving Berlin

They Can't Take That Away From Me

Music and Lyrics by George Gershwin and Ira Gershwin

The way you wear your hat, the way you sip your tea,

Oh! Look At Me Now

Words by John De Vries
Music by Joe Bushkin